This Boxer Books paperback belongs to

. . . .

www.boxerbooks.com

Reindeer
Pig
Porcupine
Toucan
Flamingo
Crocodile

Call Me Gorgeous!

Written by

Giles Milton

Illustrated by

Alexandra Milton

BOXER BOOKS

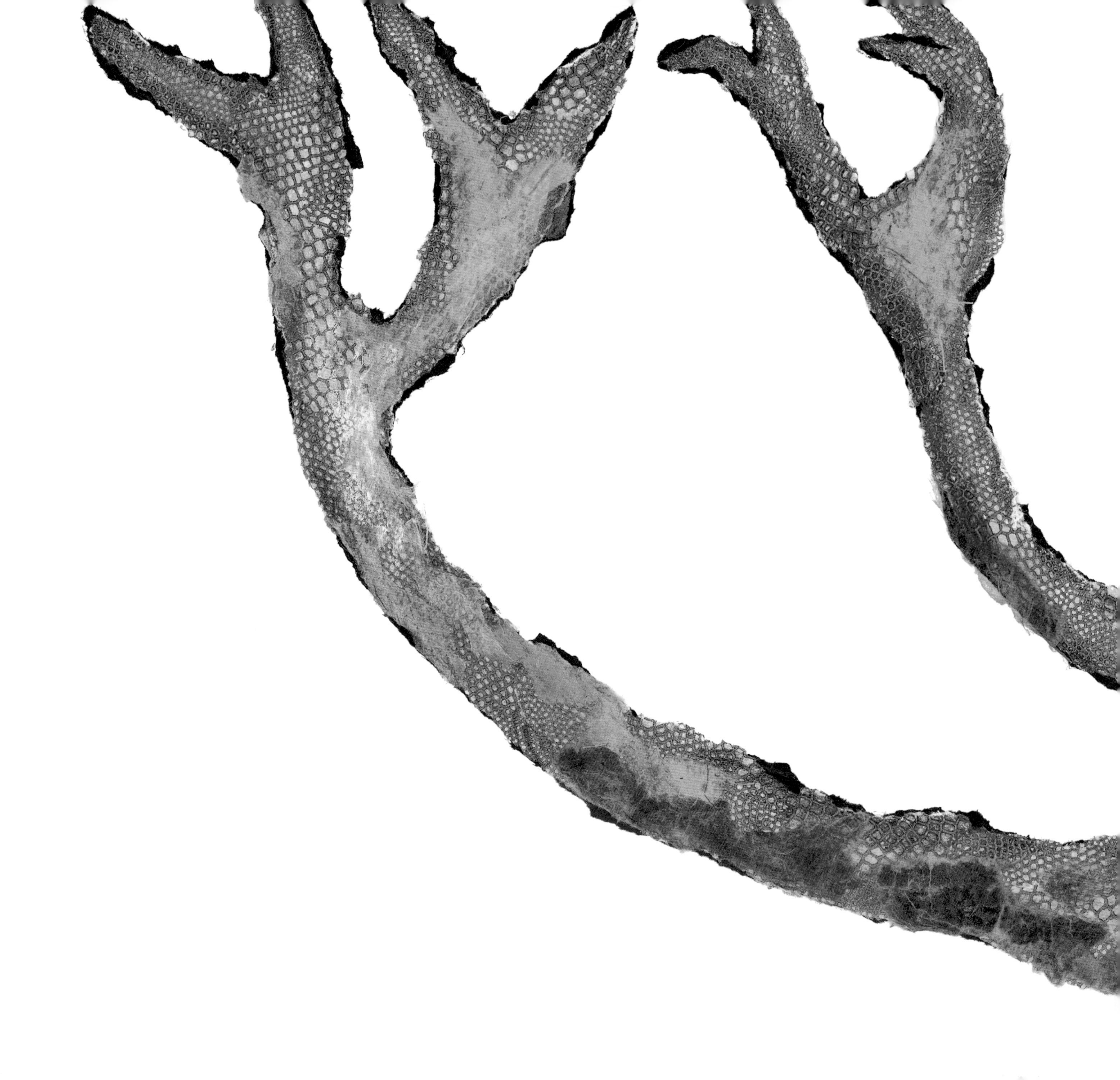

I've got
reindeer antlers

and the ears of a pig.

A porcupine's spines

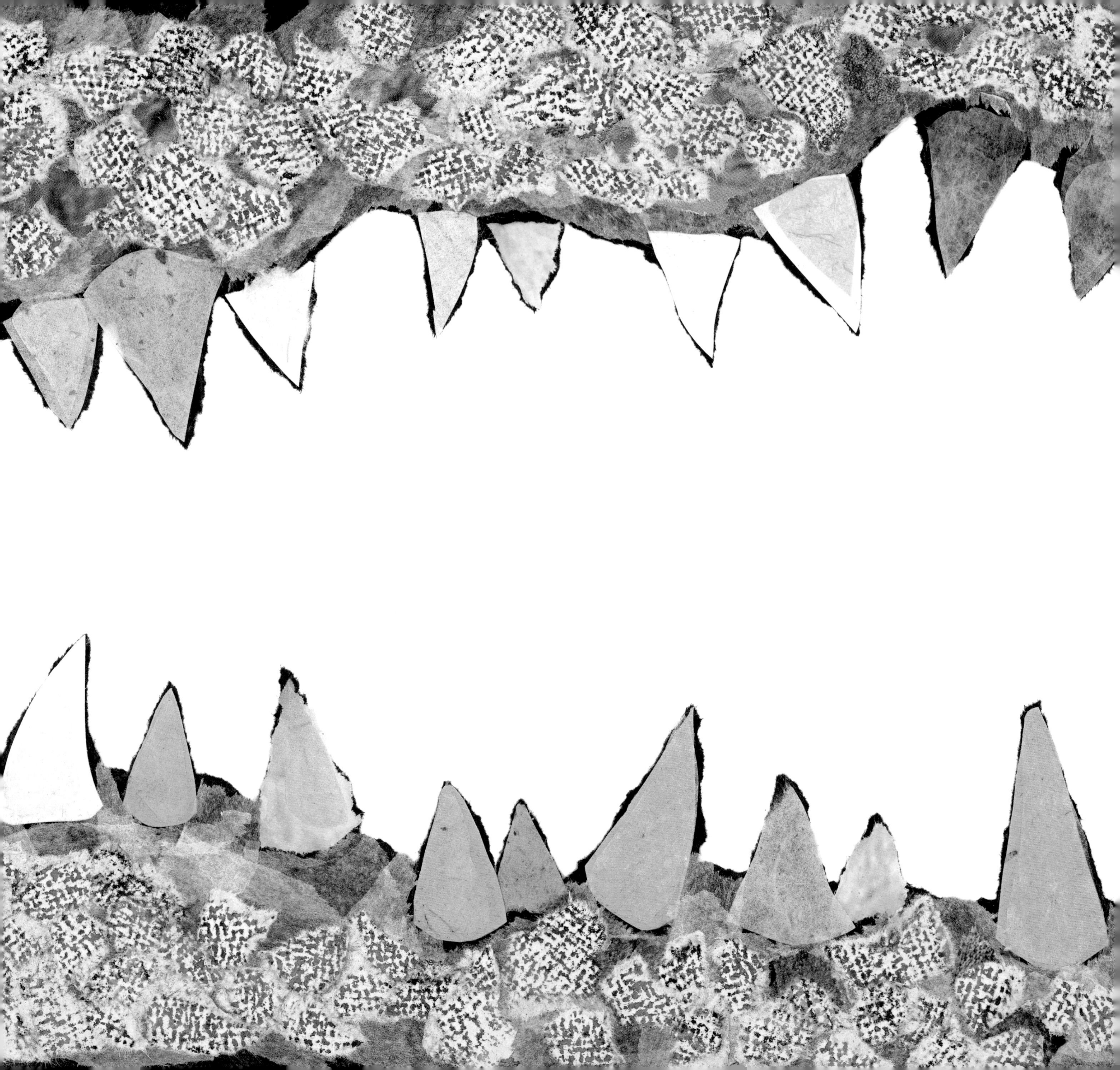

and a
crocodile's teeth.

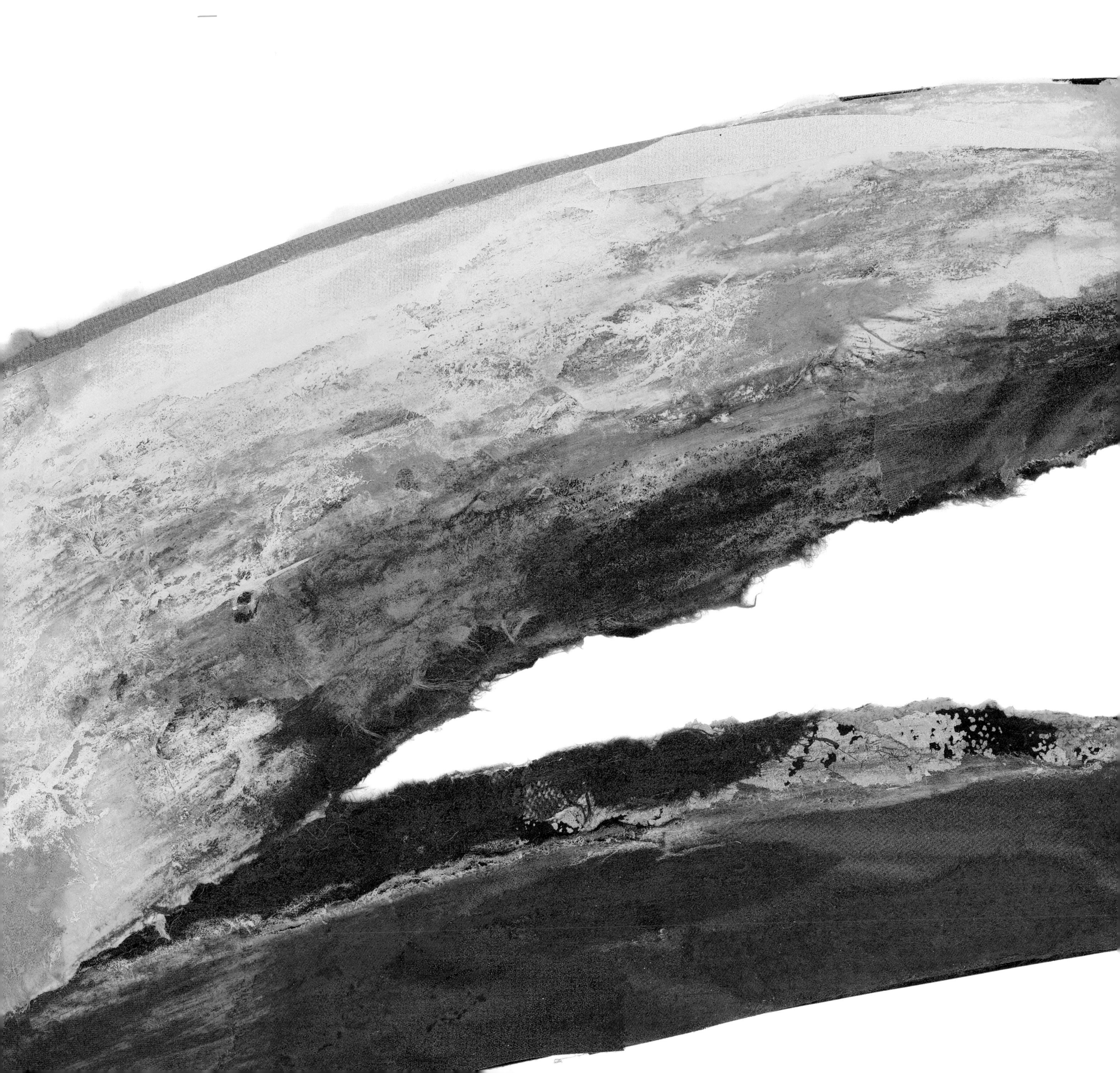

A toucan's beak

a flamingo's neck

and a
cockerel's feet.

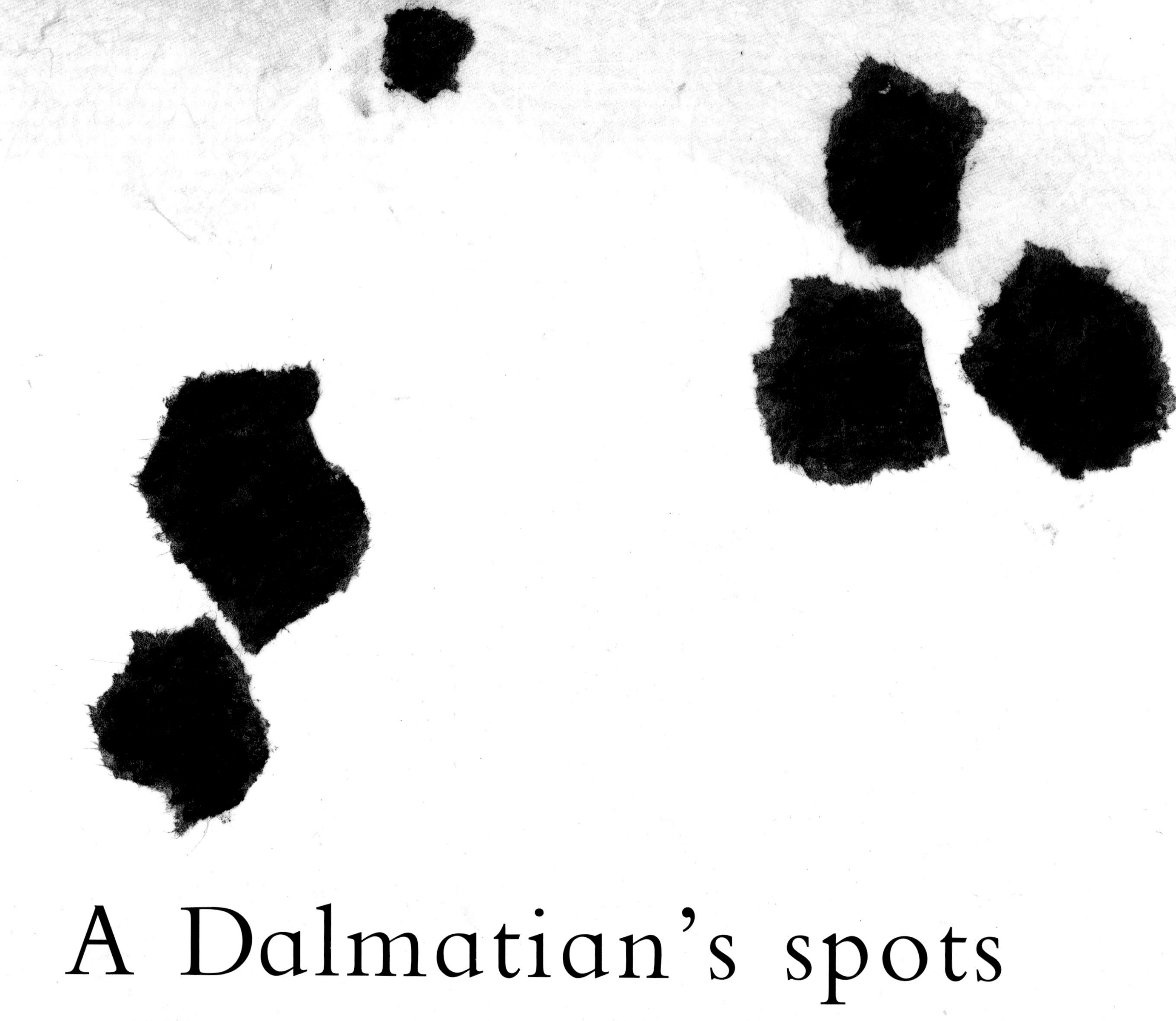

A Dalmatian's spots

and a
chameleon’s tail.

The wings of a bat

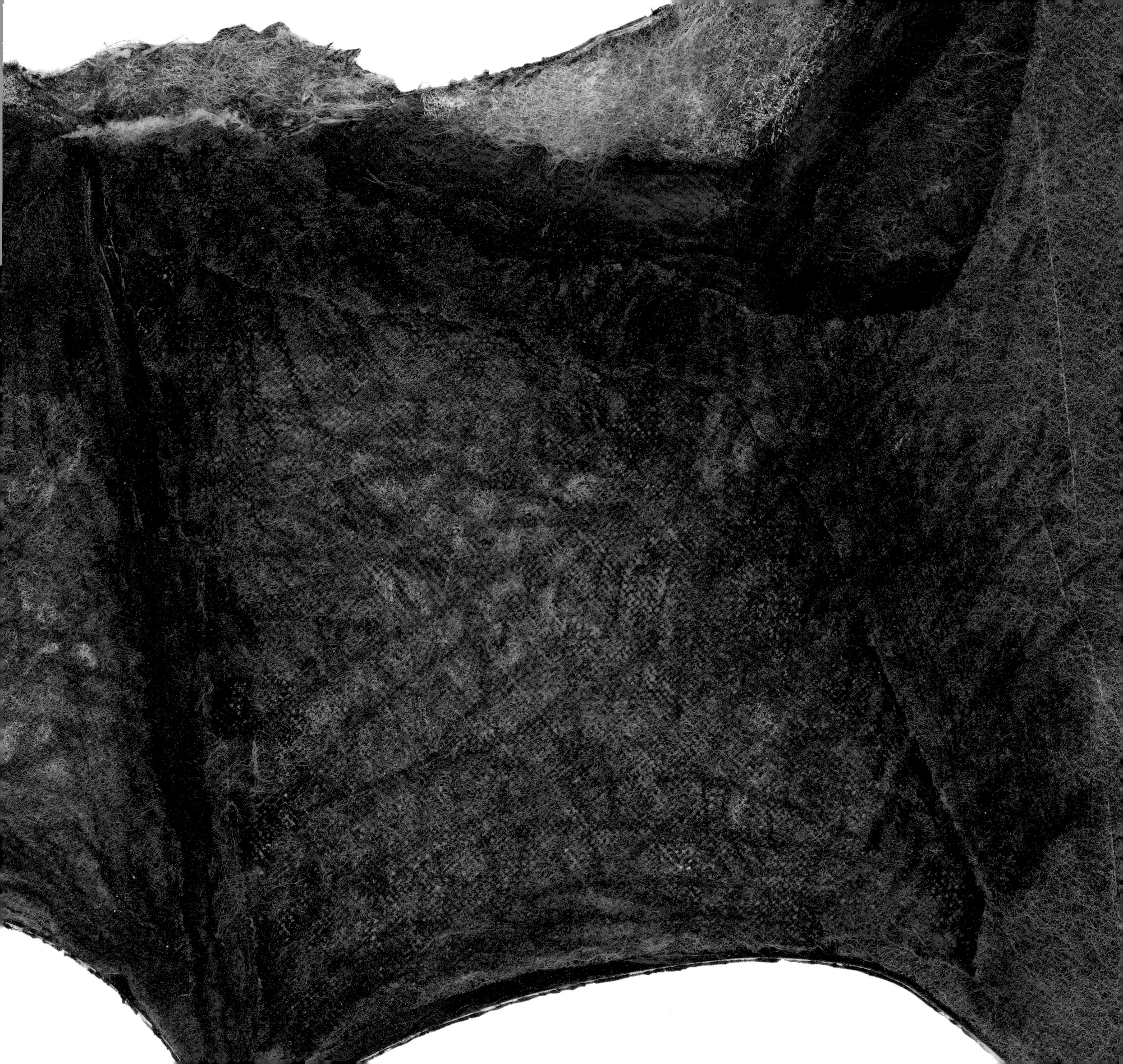

and the
eyes of a frog.

I'm a reinde-piggy-
porcu-croco-touca-
flami-cocker-
dalma-chameleo-
bat-frog.

But...

you can call me

GORGEOUS!

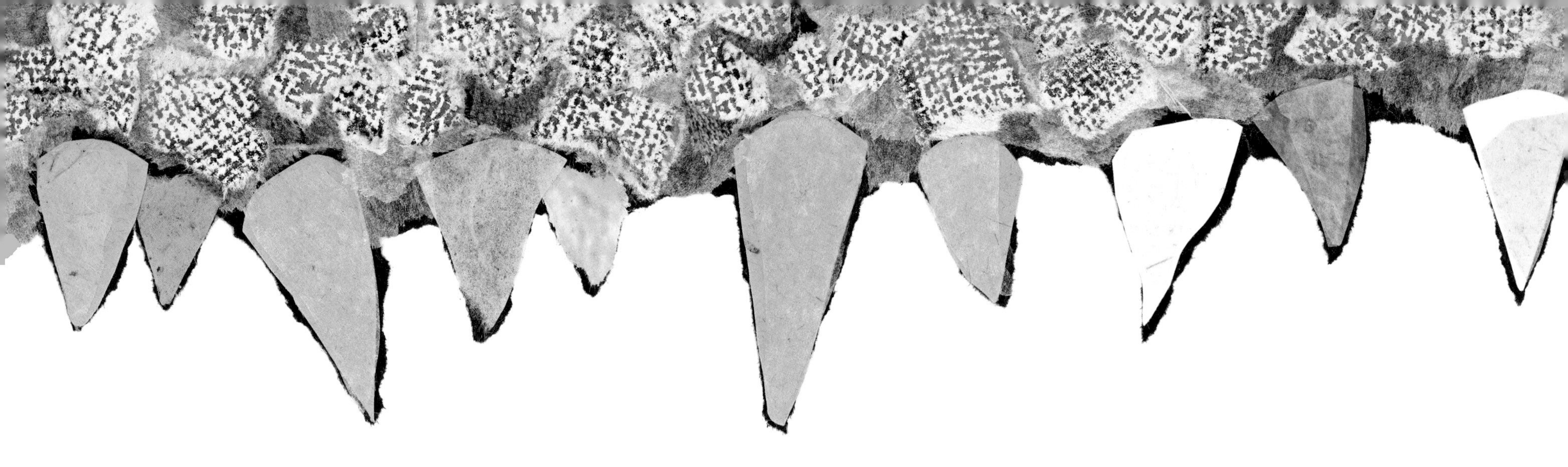

For Madeleine, Héloïse, Aurélia – all gorgeous.
Giles and Alexandra Milton

First published in hardback in Great Britain in 2009 by Boxer Books Limited.
First published in paperback in Great Britain in 2010 by Boxer Books Limited.
www.boxerbooks.com

 A CIP catalogue record for this book is available from the British Library upon request.

The illustrations were prepared using colour pencils and handmade paper from around the world. The text is set in Bembo Schoolbook.

ISBN 978-1-907152-62-7

1 3 5 7 9 10 8 6 4 2

Printed in China

All of our papers are sourced from managed forests and renewable resources.

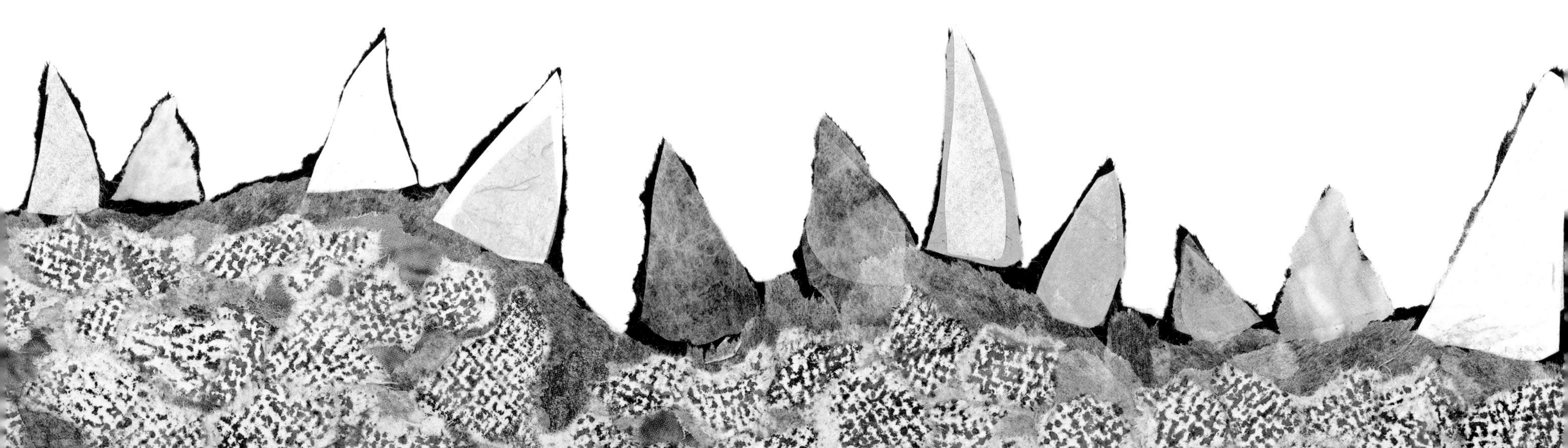

Cockerel

Dalmatian

Chameleon

Bat

Frog

Other Boxer Books paperbacks

Boys Are Best! • **Manuela Olten**

A fun and irreverent story, told from the point of view of two opinionated young boys. The boys think girls are silly scaredy cats, but they turn out be far from brave themselves when the subject of ghosts is brought up.

ISBN 978-1-905417-66-7

Chicky Chicky Chook Chook • **Cathy MacLennan**

Chicky chicks, buzzy bees and kitty cats romp in sun and snuggle in the warmth, until pitter-patter, down comes the rain. A great read-aloud, sing-along book, full of fun-to-imitate animal sounds, rhythm and movement.

ISBN 978-1-905417-32-2

Little Smudge • **Lionel Le Néouanic**

A simple, elegant and innovative tale about the importance of mixing, making friends and appreciating differences. The illustrations cleverly incorporate shapes from well-known paintings, creating a charming tale that offers a gentle introduction to modern art.

ISBN 978-1-905417-23-0

LAB LOGISTICS AND SAFETY

TAKING CARE!

SAFETY IN THE LAB

KATHLEEN A. KLATTE

PowerKiDS press
New York

Published in 2021 by The Rosen Publishing Group, Inc.
29 East 21st Street, New York, NY 10010

First Edition

Editor: Jane Katirgis
Book Design: Reann Nye

Photo Credits: Cover Andrew Brookes/Cultura/Getty Images; series art Triff/Shutterstock.com; p. 5 hxdbzxy/iStock/Getty Images Plus/Getty Images; p. 7 Air Images/Shutterstock.com; p. 9 Klaus Vedfelt/DigitalVision/Getty Images; p. 11 New Africa/Shutterstock.com; p. 13 Omer N Raja/Shutterstock.com; p. 14 Alexxndr/Shutterstock.com; p. 15 Hero Images/Getty Images; p. 17 Make.IT.Fun/Shutterstock.com; p. 19 sirtravelalot/Shutterstock.com; p. 21 science photo/Shutterstock.com; p. 22 wavebreakmedia/Shutterstock.com.

Cataloging-in-Publication Data

Names: Klatte, Kathleen A.
Title: Taking care! safety in the lab / Kathleen A. Klatte.
Description: New York : PowerKids Press, 2021. | Series: Lab logistics and safety | Includes glossary and index.
Identifiers: ISBN 9781725310469 (pbk.) | ISBN 9781725310483 (library bound) | ISBN 9781725310476 (6 pack)
Subjects: LCSH: Science rooms and equipment–Safety measures–Juvenile literature. | Laboratories–Safety measures–Juvenile literature. | Science–Experiments–Safety measures–Juvenile literature. | Science–Study and teaching–Juvenile literature.
Classification: LCC LB3325.S35 K53 2021 | DDC 502.8'4–dc23

Manufactured in the United States of America

Some of the images in this book illustrate individuals who are models. The depictions do not imply actual situations or events.

CPSIA Compliance Information: Batch #CSPK20. For Further Information contact Rosen Publishing, New York, New York at 1-800-237-9932.

CONTENTS

THE PLACE WHERE SCIENCE HAPPENS

A laboratory, or lab, is a special room that's used for science experiments. A science lab in your school has much in common with labs found in colleges, hospitals, and big companies. Labs should be arranged to be safe, clean, and organized. Doctors and scientists follow many of the same safety practices that kids learn in school.

Many of the things that help keep people safe in the lab also help them practice better science. Keeping things neat and clean and taking good notes of an experiment keep you safe. They also help other people understand the results of your work.

IN THE LAB!

You aren't allowed to eat in a lab. You might spill something on your food that can make you sick, or you might spill food in your experiment and mess up your results!

This school lab looks like a **professional** lab. The counters are easy to clean, and there's no clutter.

THE PROCESS OF SAFE DISCOVERY

A purpose of science is to learn more about how the world works. Scientists begin by asking questions. Then they perform experiments to try to answer those questions. An experiment must be performed many times, with the same results, before other scientists accept those results.

Scientists take very thorough notes at every step of an experiment in order to make sure that other people can repeat it. They're very careful that every surface and tool they use is clean, and they measure very carefully. Knowing exactly what someone was working with can be very important if an accident happens in the lab.

The **metric system** is the standard used for weights and measures throughout most of the world. In the United States, it's common to use measurements based on the old **British imperial system**, or sometimes both. When you perform an experiment, it's important to note which system you used.

SAFETY ALWAYS

The idea of performing an experiment is very exciting, and you'll probably want to get started right away. However, the first step to working in a lab is to keep calm, slow down, and pay attention to your teacher's directions. Raise your hand and ask questions if you don't understand something. Read any written directions carefully, then read them again, and ask questions until you're ready to start.

Next, you'll want to gather all the things you'll need for your experiment. Be sure to walk, not run! Labs contain glass **equipment** and **substances** that can spill.

These kids are listening carefully while their teacher explains the experiment they're going to work on.

KEEPING YOURSELF SAFE

The instructions for an experiment should always list what sort of personal safety equipment you need to use. This is for your protection, but it also helps you practice good science.

Lab coats and gloves protect you from being splashed with chemicals, but they also protect your experiment. Your clothes might have hair from your pet or pollen from your garden. If these things drop into your experiment, they can change the results. Oils or dead skin cells from your hands can also affect your experiment.

Your teacher might also instruct you to tie back your hair and wear rubber-soled, closed-toe shoes in the lab.

This young scientist is wearing safety glasses and gloves to protect her eyes and hands from the chemicals she's working with.

A SAFE PLACE FOR SCIENCE

All labs contain a lot of safety equipment that you can easily identify. This includes things such as **fire extinguishers**, first-aid kits, and **eyewash stations**. There's probably a rubber mat in front of the sink so no one slips on a wet floor.

In the event of a spill or an accident in the lab, the most important thing to do is to tell a teacher immediately, then follow their instructions.

There are special tools for your teacher to use to pick up broken glass or clean up spilled chemicals. All of these items should be clearly marked with big, bright labels, so they can be easily found in an **emergency**.

IN THE LAB!

There are lots of signs in a lab. Safety equipment should always be clearly marked, and so should **dangerous** items. The most important sign to know is the one that marks the fire exit.

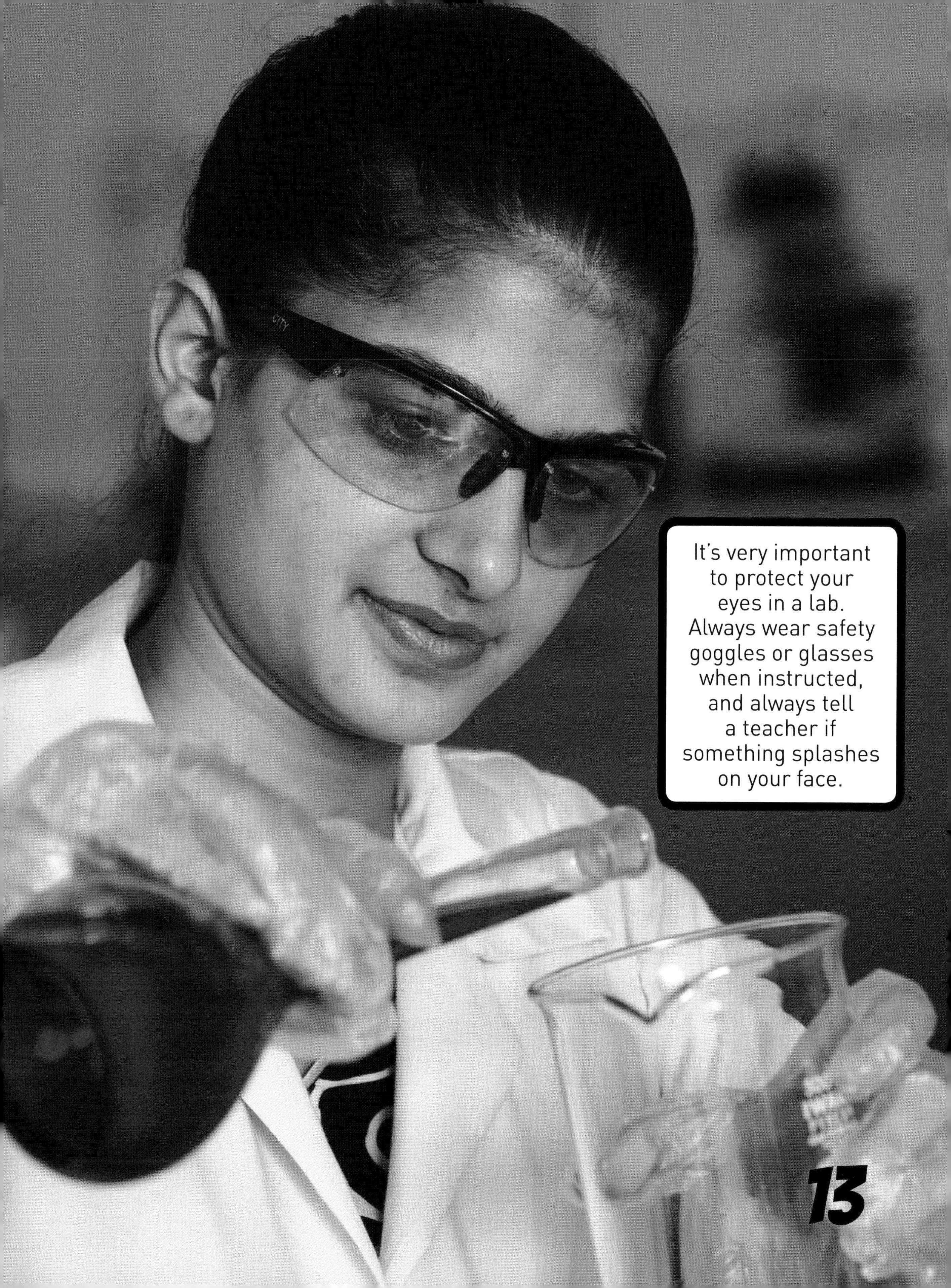

It's very important to protect your eyes in a lab. Always wear safety goggles or glasses when instructed, and always tell a teacher if something splashes on your face.

NEAT, CLEAN, AND ORGANIZED

Keeping your workspace neat and organized is one of the best ways to keep safe in the lab. You should only have the things that you're working with in front of you during an experiment. Put things away as you finish with them.

Put away your phone! A lab is a very bad place to be **distracted**.

Taking clear notes as you work is good safety and good science. If your experiment doesn't turn out like your classmates' experiments, your notes can help you figure out what you each did differently. If you get hurt, your notes can help other people figure out how to help you.

Use a lab notebook to record notes during your experiment. You can also write the results of your experiment.

OOPS! ACCIDENTS HAPPEN

No matter how careful you are, things sometimes go wrong in a lab. The most important thing for you to do is to keep calm and tell your teacher right away.

Be sure you tell your teacher if you spill something on the floor or break glass. Your teacher will help you use the correct safety equipment to clean up the spill before someone gets hurt.

Never try to force a glass rod through a rubber stopper. The glass could break and cause a serious cut. Always tell your teacher right away if you cut yourself on broken glass or get splashed with anything. Your teacher will make sure you get help.

IN THE LAB!

One of the best ways to prevent accidents in the lab is to keep the floors clear, so people don't trip and fall. Always put away your coats and bags.

You could get hurt if you try to clean this up yourself. Get a teacher, who will show you which tools to use.

WHAT COULD GO WRONG?

Because science is all about discovery and exploration, you might wonder why there are so many safety rules to follow. The answer is that people learn from experience.

Marie Curie was a famous scientist who won two Nobel Prizes for her discoveries about **radioactivity**. She died of cancer, a serious illness that was probably caused by **radiation** in her lab. Today, scientists who work with radiation use special protective gear and wear badges, or tags, that measure radiation exposure.

In the past, many scientists died or suffered severe injuries, or wounds, from breathing in or even tasting chemicals. Learn from their stories, and always wear protective gear.

IN THE LAB!

The Bunsen burner is a standard piece of lab equipment named for 19th-century scientist Robert Bunsen. Aside from his many discoveries, Bunsen is also known for losing the sight in his right eye because he'd been working without eye protection.

These scientists have learned from accidents that happened in the past. They're wearing the proper safety gear.

FAMOUS LAB "ACCIDENTS"

Sometimes an experiment doesn't work quite as expected. Good safety practices and notes can mean the difference between a terrible accident and an exciting new discovery.

In 1968, a man named Spencer Silver was trying to invent a new strong glue. Instead, he invented a very weak one. Several years later, someone thought of a good use for it. Spencer Silver had followed good lab practices, so his method could be repeated. Today, his glue is used on Post-it Notes, one of the most common office supplies.

Super Glue, cornflakes, and safety glass are other products that people discovered accidentally.

IN THE LAB!

When someone invents a new drug, it must go through many safety tests. Sometimes during testing, it turns out that a drug works differently than scientists thought it would. Minoxidil was invented as a treatment for high blood pressure, but now it's marketed as a product for growing hair.

Alexander Fleming found some interesting **mold** growing on his lab dishes when he returned from a vacation in 1928. This would lead to the discovery of penicillin, one of the first antibiotics.

SAFETY EQUALS GOOD SCIENCE

History is filled with stories of people who made wonderful discoveries. It's also filled with stories of terrible things that happened because people weren't careful.

Saccharine, an artificial sweetener, was discovered by accident because a scientist forgot to wash his hands. He figured out which chemical was so sweet by tasting what he'd been working with. He was very lucky that he didn't poison himself! Taking good notes and following safety rules would have been much better—and safer.

Learning and discovering new things about the world we live in should always be fun and exciting. Keeping yourself safe is the best way to make that happen.

GLOSSARY

British imperial system: The traditional system of weights and measures used officially in Great Britain from 1824 until the adoption of the metric system beginning in 1965.

dangerous: Not safe.

distracted: To be unable to think about or pay attention to something; unable to concentrate.

emergency: An unexpected and usually dangerous situation that calls for immediate action.

equipment: Supplies or tools needed for a certain purpose.

eyewash station: A special kind of sink for rinsing away things that have splashed in your eyes.

fire extinguisher: A metal container filled with chemicals that is used to put out a fire.

metric system: A decimal system of weights and measures based on the meter and the kilogram.

mold: A substance that grows on the surface of damp or rotting things.

professional: Having to do with a job somebody does for a living.

radiation: Waves of energy.

radioactivity: The production of a powerful and dangerous kind of energy called radiation.

substance: Matter of a particular kind.

INDEX

Due to the changing nature of Internet links, PowerKids Press has developed an online list of websites related to the subject of this book. This site is updated regularly. Please use this link to access the list: www.powerkidslinks.com/lls/safety